# Consonant Pretest

"X" it.

(See Teacher's Key for Books 1 to 5.)

| | | | |
|---|---|---|---|
| **f** | | | |
| **k** | | | |
| **r** | | | |
| **t** | | | |
| **l** | | | |
| **g** | | | |

i

**Consonant Pretest**

"X" it.

| v | | | |
|---|---|---|---|
| h | | | |
| s | | | |
| d | | | |
| j | | | |
| z | | | |
| c | | | |

ii

# Explode The Code® 1

*Essential lessons for phonics mastery*

Nancy Hall • Rena Price

**School Specialty, Inc.**

Cambridge and Toronto

**Cover Design:** Hugh Price
**Text illustrations:** Laura Price and Alan Price

Printed in Mayfield, PA, in July 2012
ISBN 978-0-8388-1460-4

16  17  18  19  20  PAH  16  15  14  13  12

## Consonant Pretest

"X" it.

| | | | |
|---|---|---|---|
| **b** | | | |
| **w** | | | |
| **m** | | | |
| **y** | | | |
| **p** | | | |
| **qu** | | | |
| **n** | | | |

*For further practice with consonants, see Primers for the Explode the Code series.

# a says /ă/ as in

Find the picture that begins with
the sound of the letter below.
"X" it.

| ă | | | |
|---|---|---|---|
| ă | | | |
| ă | | | |
| ă | | | |
| ă | | | |
| ă | | | |

"X" the same word.

| | | |
|---|---|---|
| bat | hat | ~~bat~~ |
| fat | hat | ~~fat~~ |
| mat | ~~mat~~ | nat |
| pat | bat | ~~pat~~ |
| rat | rap | ~~rat~~ |
| cat | cot | ~~cat~~ |
| sat | ~~sat~~ | sap |

2

Follow the arrows to write the letter **a**, which says /ă/ as in 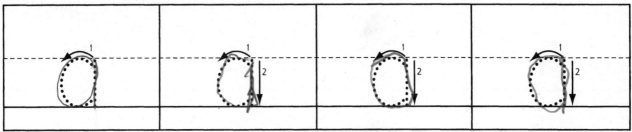.
Say the sound aloud.
Notice that **a** begins like the letter **c**.

Notice that **a** is only one space tall. Trace the letters.

Trace and copy the letter that begins the pictured word.

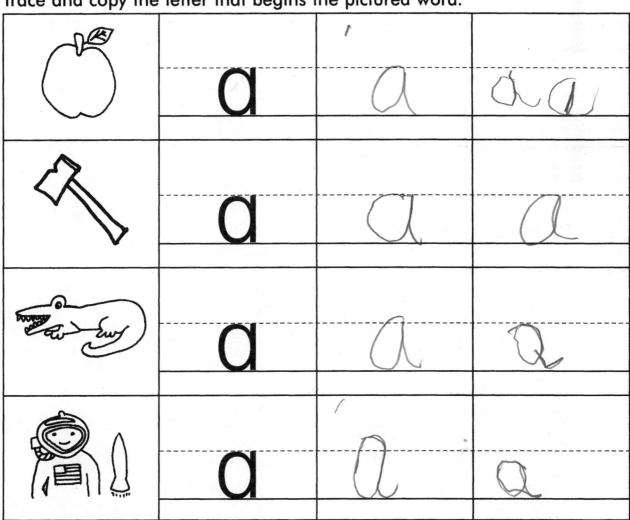

Read, copy, and "X" it.

| bat | | | |
|---|---|---|---|
| b a t | | | |
| hat | | | |
| ___ ___ ___ | | | |
| sat | | | |
| ___ ___ ___ | | | |
| rat | | | |
| ___ ___ ___ | | | |
| Nat | | | |
| ___ ___ ___ | | | |
| bat | | | |
| ___ ___ ___ | | | |
| mat | | | |
| ___ ___ ___ | | | |

| | Spell. | | | Write. |
|---|---|---|---|---|
| | ⓑ g | ⓐ n | f ⓣ | **bat** |
| | s r | n a | t m | |
| | h b | o a | t p | |
| | g p | a x | t d | |
| | w m | i a | k t | |
| | c d | m a | t h | |
| | p b | a r | t d | |

5

**Match and write it.**

hat     b~~a~~t     mat     bat

pat     rat     sat     cat

bat
_____

_____

_____

_____

_____

_____

_____

◯ it.

bad

fat

(bat)

| | |
|---|---|
| rat | can |
| ran | cat |
| tar | cab |
| nap | man |
| tan | tam |
| Nat | mat |
| pat | cat |
| bat | sad |
| pad | sat |

"X" it.

| | | |
|---|---|---|
| The hat is fat.<br><br>The bat is fat. | ☐<br>☒ | |
| Pat sat on a cat.<br><br>Pat sat on a mat. | ☐<br>☐ | |
| A cat is at bat.<br><br>A rat is at bat. | ☐<br>☐ | |
| The cat is on a mat.<br><br>The rat is on a cat. | ☐<br>☐ | |
| Nat sat at bat.<br><br>Nat sat on a rat. | ☐<br>☐ | |
| A fat bat is on a cat.<br><br>A fat cat is on a hat. | ☐<br>☐ | |
| The rat sat.<br><br>The bat sat. | ☐<br>☐ | |

8

Write it.

bat

**Lesson 2**

# a says /ă/ as in

Find the picture that begins with
the sound of the letter below.
"X" it.

| ă | | | |
|---|---|---|---|
| ă | | | |
| ă | | | |
| ă | | | |
| ă | | | |
| ă | | | |

"X" the same word.

| | | |
|---|---|---|
| fan | ban | ~~fan~~ |
| can | con | can |
| had | lad | had |
| ran | ram | ran |
| tan | nat | tan |
| bad | dad | bad |
| pan | pan | ban |

**Read, copy, and "X" it.**

| | | | |
|---|---|---|---|
| fan <br> f a n | | | |
| can <br> __ __ __ | | | |
| dad <br> __ __ __ | | | |
| Pam <br> __ __ __ | | | |
| mad <br> __ __ __ | | | |
| cat <br> __ __ __ | | | |
| ran <br> __ __ __ | | | |

| | Spell. | | | Write. |
|---|---|---|---|---|
| | (f)  l  (a)  c  i  (n) | | | **fan** |
| | m  n  a  d  m  n | | | |
| | k  s  c  a  d  g | | | |
| | r  w  a  k  n  t | | | |
| | p  v  g  a  d  n | | | |
| | r  j  c  a  t  n | | | |
| | t  h  a  c  t  m | | | |

fat

⬭ fan

man

| | |
|---|---|
| dad | |
| had | |
| bat | |

| | |
|---|---|
| Jam | |
| Jan | |
| Tap | |

| | |
|---|---|
| can | |
| cat | |
| car | |

| | |
|---|---|
| dad | |
| bat | |
| tab | |

| | |
|---|---|
| fad | |
| sat | |
| sad | |

| | |
|---|---|
| fan | |
| rat | |
| ran | |

**Match and write it.**

fan      hat      bat      can

pan      man      mad      sad

fan

"X" it.

| | | |
|---|---|---|
| The cat is fat. | ☒ | |
| A rat is sad. | ☐ | |
| The cat is mad. | ☐ | |
| The hat is mad. | ☐ | |
| The fan ran. | ☐ | |
| The man ran. | ☐ | |
| The mat is sad. | ☐ | |
| The rat is sad. | ☐ | |
| Sam has a can. | ☐ | |
| Sam has a cat. | ☐ | |
| The fat rat bats. | ☐ | |
| Pat is at bat. | ☐ | |
| The can sat in the pan. | ☐ | |
| The man had a fan. | ☐ | |

Write it.

fan

# a says /ă/ as in

Find the picture that begins with
the sound of the letter below.
"X" it.

| ă | | | |
|---|---|---|---|
| ă | | | |
| ă | | | |
| ă | | | |
| ă | | | |
| ă | | | |

"X" the same word.

| | | |
|---|---|---|
| bag | gab | ~~bag~~ |
| gas | gab | gas |
| ban | dan | ban |
| had | had | hag |
| fad | lad | fad |
| map | nap | map |
| jam | jan | jam |

Read, copy, and "X" it.

| | | | |
|---|---|---|---|
| **bag** <u>b a g</u> | | | |
| **pal** ___ ___ ___ | | | |
| **cap** ___ ___ ___ | | | |
| **tag** ___ ___ ___ | | | |
| **fan** ___ ___ ___ | | | |
| **rat** ___ ___ ___ | | | |
| **wag** ___ ___ ___ | | | |

20

| | | | |
|---|---|---|---|
| ⓑ g | c | ⓐ | ⓖ j | **bag** |
| r n | a | o | p t | |
| m w | a | c | p t | |
| g d | b | a | n s | |
| f t | d | a | n m | |
| r n | c | a | b t | |
| g c | a | o | m p | |

bad

(bag)

gab

sap

pass

pan

Al

At

Ax

sag

sap

nap

tap

tag

hag

pad

pan

pal

mitt

mat

sat

Match and write it.

| | | | |
|---|---|---|---|
| sat | nap | wag | ~~bag~~ |
| mat | Pam | gas | tag |

bag

"X" it.

| | | |
|---|---|---|
| A rat naps in a cap. | ☒ | |
| The man pats a cat. | ☐ | |
| Sam has a bag. | ☐ | |
| The rat is in the pan. | ☐ | |
| A bass is at bat. | ☐ | |
| A cat is at bat. | ☐ | |
| Pat has a nap. | ☐ | |
| Pat has a fan. | ☐ | |
| A rat sat on Pam. | ☐ | |
| A cat sat in a bag. | ☐ | |
| Al has a cap. | ☐ | |
| Al has a pal. | ☐ | |
| The bat can wag. | ☐ | |
| The hat has a tag. | ☐ | |

**Write it.**

bag

## Lesson 4

# i says /ĭ/ as in

Find the picture that begins with
the sound of the letter below.
"X" it.

Follow the arrows to write the letter **i**, which says /ĭ/ as in .
Say the sound aloud.

Notice that **i** is only one space tall. Trace the letters.

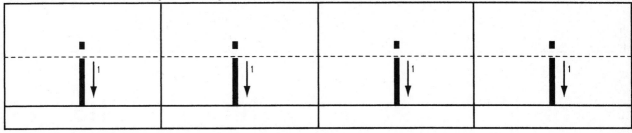

Trace and copy the letter that begins the pictured word.

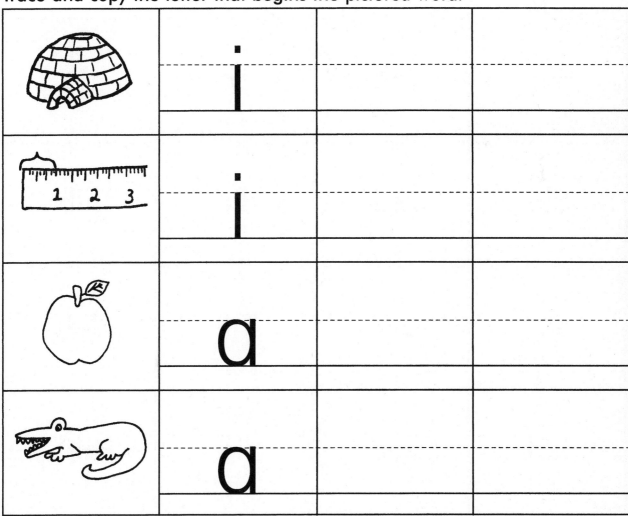

"X" the same word.

| | | | |
|---|---|---|---|
| bill | pin | din | ~~bill~~ |
| fit | lit | fit | fill |
| his | sit | his | has |
| tin | tim | nit | tin |
| did | bid | did | bib |
| Jill | Jill | Till | Jell |
| hid | mid | lid | hid |

28

Read, copy, and "X" it.

| | | | |
|---|---|---|---|
| pig<br><br>p i g | | | |
| hill<br><br>_ _ _ _ | | | |
| wig<br><br>_ _ _ _ | $\begin{array}{r} 2 \\ + \ 2 \\ \hline 4 \end{array}$ | | |
| Jim<br><br>_ _ _ _ | | | |
| bit<br><br>_ _ _ _ | | | |
| win<br><br>_ _ _ _ | | | |
| dig<br><br>_ _ _ _ | | | |

Match and write it.

| pig | win | wig | ~~lip~~ |
|-----|-----|-----|------|
| mitt | fin | sit | pin |

lip

| | | | | | |
|---|---|---|---|---|---|
| | (h)  b | a  (i) | m  (ll) | **hill** |
| | b  p | i  j | g  p | |
| | m  n | i  a | tt  l | |
| | d  b | n  i | p  g | |
| | b  d | i  j | t  k | |
| | w  m | i  t | g  p | |
| | n  p | i  a | n  m | |

sad

sit

(sip)

| | |
|---|---|
| hit | dig |
| hat | bib |
| hill | big |

| | |
|---|---|
| hat | wit |
| fill | sit |
| fin | sill |

| | |
|---|---|
| mat | fill |
| mitt | hit |
| mill | hill |

"X" it.

| | | |
|---|---|---|
| A pig is big.<br>A pin is big. | ☐<br>☒ | |
| Lin bit the can.<br>Lin hit the can. | ☐<br>☐ | |
| The man can dig.<br>The man can sit. | ☐<br>☐ | |
| The fin is big.<br>The pin is big. | ☐<br>☐ | |
| Pam has a big pig.<br>Pam has a bad wig. | ☐<br>☐ | |
| Jim sits on a pin.<br>Jim sat on a pan. | ☐<br>☐ | |
| Pat has big hats.<br>Pat has a big mitt. | ☐<br>☐ | |

Write it.

hill

Find the picture that begins with the sound of each letter below. "X" it.

ă =          ĭ =

| | | | |
|---|---|---|---|
| **ă** | | | |
| **ĭ** | | | |
| **ă** | | | |
| **ĭ** | | | |
| **ă** | | | |
| **ĭ** | | 2 + 2 = 4 | |

"X" the same word.

| | | | |
|---|---|---|---|
| pan | pin | ~~pan~~ | din |
| wig | wig | wag | wit |
| lid | lad | lid | lib |
| dad | dad | dab | bad |
| sat | sit | sat | sad |
| tin | tan | tin | nit |
| has | his | has | hag |

36

Read, copy, and "X" it.

| pan  p a n | | | |
|---|---|---|---|
| bag  _ _ _ | | | |
| win  _ _ _ | | | |
| wig  _ _ _ | | | |
| mad  _ _ _ | | | |
| sip  _ _ _ | | | |
| lip  _ _ _ | | | |

37

| | | | | |
|---|---|---|---|---|
| | b (p) (a) i m (n) | | | **pan** |
| | l f i a n m | | | |
| | b d i a p g | | | |
| | w m a i q g | | | |
| | l t i a t p | | | |
| | p w a i t n | | | |
| | l s a i p d | | | |

◯ it.

| | |
|---|---|
| | pin |
| | fan |
| | (pan) |

| | | | |
|---|---|---|---|
| | bat | | hill |
| | tab | | Jill |
| | bit | | jam |

| | | | |
|---|---|---|---|
| 2 + 2 = 4 | odd | | wig |
| | add | | wag |
| | ill | | bag |

| | | | |
|---|---|---|---|
| | ball | | bib |
| | bit | | lap |
| | Bill | | big |

"X" it.

| | | |
|---|---|---|
| The mat is big.<br><br>The wig is big. | ☐<br>☒ | |
| Bill can add.<br><br>His hat is a lid. | ☐<br>☐ | |
| Dad has a big pin.<br><br>Dad has big lips. | ☐<br>☐ | |
| The cat has a fan.<br><br>The cap has a fin. | ☐<br>☐ | |
| Jill has a big mitt.<br><br>Jill sits on a mat. | ☐<br>☐ | |
| The big rat wins.<br><br>The rat sips jam. | ☐<br>☐ | |
| Pat bit the tin pig.<br><br>A tin pig bit Pat. | ☐<br>☐ | |

40

Write it.

pan

*For further practice on short a in combination, see Book 1½, pp. 17–24.

41

# Lesson 6

## u says /ŭ/ as in

Find the picture that begins with
the sound of the letter below.
"X" it.

| | | | |
|---|---|---|---|
| Ŭ | | | |
| Ŭ | | | |
| Ŭ | | | |
| Ŭ | | | |
| Ŭ | | | |
| Ŭ | | | |

"X" the same word.

| | | | |
|---|---|---|---|
| hug | dug | ~~hug~~ | bug |
| rub | rib | rut | rub |
| hum | hum | ham | mum |
| fun | fan | hum | fun |
| tug | lug | tug | tag |
| gum | mug | bug | gum |
| but | but | tub | bat |

Read, copy, and "X" it.

| hug <br> h u g | | | |
|---|---|---|---|
| bug <br> _ _ _ | | | |
| sub <br> _ _ _ | | | |
| run <br> _ _ _ | | | |
| rug <br> _ _ _ | | | |
| pup <br> _ _ _ | | | |
| bus <br> _ _ _ | | | |

44

Follow the arrows to write the letter **u**, which says /ŭ/ as in  .
Say the sound aloud.

Notice that **u** is only one space tall. Trace the letters.

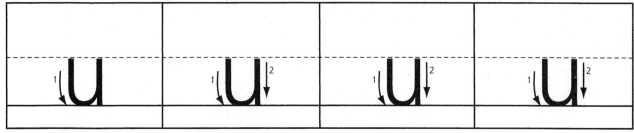

Trace and copy the letter that begins the pictured word.

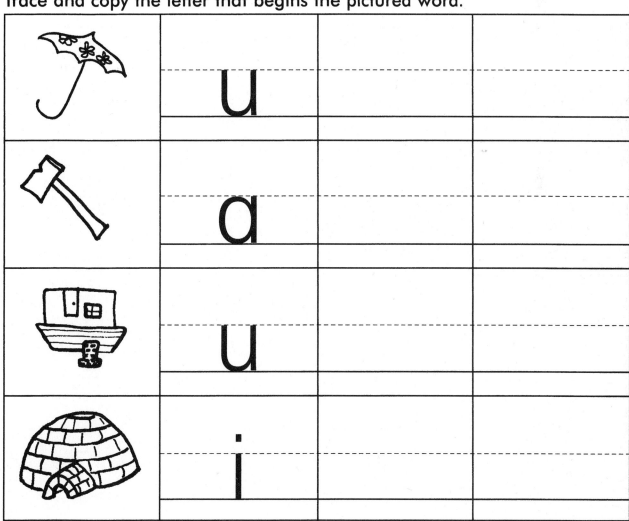

Match and write it.

| rug | ~~hug~~ | sun | gum |
| bus | bug | run | cup |

| hug | ____ ____ ____ |
| ____ ____ ____ | ____ ____ ____ |
| ____ ____ ____ | ____ ____ ____ |
| ____ ____ ____ | ____ ____ ____ |

Spell.                                           Write.

| | | | | |
|---|---|---|---|---|
| | b (h) (u) a p (g) | | | **hu** |
| | p g u n b p | | | |
| | a s u a m n | | | |
| | p b n u c s | | | |
| | g p a u n m | | | |
| | o c n u b p | | | |
| | b d u a p g | | | |

47

hum

( hug )

dug

mug

pan

gum

pub

pup

bug

rug

rag

mug

hut

hat

nut

sup

sip

sub

tub

tug

lug

"X" it.

| | | |
|---|---|---|
| The pup dug in the sun.<br><br>The cat sat in the sun. | ☒<br>☐ | |
| A bug is in the mud.<br><br>A bug is on Jim. | ☐<br>☐ | |
| The pup hid in the hut.<br><br>The bus hid in the hut. | ☐<br>☐ | |
| A tug is on the rug.<br><br>Tim can tug and tug. | ☐<br>☐ | |
| The sun is on the rug.<br><br>The bug is in the sun. | ☐<br>☐ | |
| The sub is in the mud.<br><br>The tub is in the sun. | ☐<br>☐ | |
| The pup sits on the cup.<br><br>A cup is on the hut. | ☐<br>☐ | |

Write it.

hug

Find the picture that begins with
the sound of each letter below.
"X" it.

| | | | |
|---|---|---|---|
| ă | | | |
| ĭ | | | |
| ŭ | | | |
| ĭ | | | |
| ŭ | | | |
| ă | | | |

Read, copy, and "X" it.

| nut n u t | | | |
|---|---|---|---|
| fill ___ ___ ___ ___ | | | |
| Ann ___ ___ ___ ___ | | | |
| bun ___ ___ ___ | | | |
| mug ___ ___ ___ | | | |
| cap ___ ___ ___ | | | |
| tub ___ ___ ___ | | | |

| | | | |
|---|---|---|---|
| (n) s | (u) n | (t) l | **nut** |
| m n | i e | t x | |
| t f | u a | d b | |
| r c | u a | g p | |
| u m | i u | g b | |
| b d | u a | n u | |
| f t | i e | ll tt | |

Match and write it.

six        fill        cut        Dan

mix       duck      ~~nut~~       fix

nut          _ _ _ _ _ _

Yes or no?

| | No | Yes |
|---|---|---|
| Can I fill a cup up? | ☐ | ☒ |
| Will a duck pass a bus? | ☐ | ☐ |
| Will a sick cat nap a bit? | ☐ | ☐ |
| Can a pig add six and six? | ☐ | ☐ |
| Is it fun to pick nuts? | ☐ | ☐ |
| Can a bag rip? | ☐ | ☐ |
| Can a bug hug a rat? | ☐ | ☐ |

nat

mutt

( nut )

cat

cut

cup

nix

max

mix

mitt

nut

mutt

bed

bud

bad

fix

tax

fin

duck

luck

back

"X" it.

| | | |
|---|---|---|
| A big mutt naps.<br><br>It is a big mug. | ☐<br>☒ | |
| The bug is on a hill.<br><br>The sub is on a hill. | ☐<br>☐ | |
| Bill sat on a mutt.<br><br>Bill sat in the bus. | ☐<br>☐ | |
| A cat hid the nut.<br><br>A rat wins a cup. | ☐<br>☐ | |
| Ann has a mitt.<br><br>Sam will mix the nuts. | ☐<br>☐ | |
| Jill naps in the bus.<br><br>Jill hid in the tub. | ☐<br>☐ | |
| Jan can fix the bus.<br><br>Jan can fit a bun in the bag. | ☐<br>☐ | |

**Write it.**

nut

*For further practice on short *a*, *i*, and *u*, see Book 1½, pp. 33–48.

# Lesson 8

## e says /ĕ/ as in

Find the picture that begins with
the sound of the letter below.
"X" it.

| ĕ | | | |
|---|---|---|---|
| ĕ | | | |
| ĕ | | | |
| ĕ | | | |
| ĕ | | | |
| ĕ | | | |

"X" the same word.

| | | | |
|---|---|---|---|
| pen | pan | ~~pen~~ | hen |
| let | led | lit | let |
| well | well | will | mill |
| red | reb | ned | red |
| beg | bag | beg | bug |
| led | leg | lid | led |
| pep | peg | pep | pip |

60

Follow the arrows to write the letter **e**, which says /ĕ/ as in  .
Say the sound aloud.

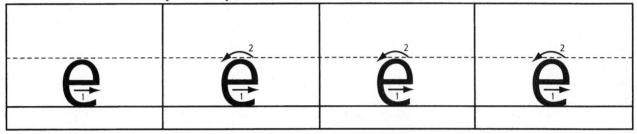

Notice that **e** is only one space tall. Trace the letters.

Trace and copy the letter that begins the pictured word.

| | e | | |
|---|---|---|---|
| | e | | |
| | u | | |
| | e | | |

Read, copy, and "X" it.

| pen p e n | | | |
|---|---|---|---|
| net ____ | | | |
| ten ____ | | | |
| fell ____ | | | |
| hen ____ | | | |
| Peg ____ | | | |
| bell ____ | | | |

| | Spell. | | | Write. |
|---|---|---|---|---|
| | (p) b | a (e) | (n) m | **pen** |
| 10 | i t | a e | m n | ___ |
| | d b | e n | p d | ___ |
| | l h | a e | g p | ___ |
| | n m | e a | t l | ___ |
| | h t | e i | m n | ___ |
| | b d | e i | ll tt | ___ |

63

Match and write it.

bed    Ted    leg    bell

fed    ~~pen~~    met    net

pen

it.

hen

(pen)

pan

led

fed

leg

mitt

miss

mess

pit

bet

pet

sip

sell

fell

Nan

men

mum

met

mat

net

| | | |
|---|---|---|
| A wet hen sits. | | |
| The pen is wet. | ☒ | |

| | | |
|---|---|---|
| Nan fell in the pen. | | |
| Nan fed the pet. | | |

| | | |
|---|---|---|
| The pet has a fin. | | |
| The net has a rip. | | |

| | | |
|---|---|---|
| Ten men fed the hen. | | |
| Al met a fat hen. | | |

| | | |
|---|---|---|
| Peg fell in the tub. | | |
| Peg will tug the bell. | | |

| | | |
|---|---|---|
| His bed is a mess. | | |
| Six men sit on a bus. | | |

| | | |
|---|---|---|
| The bugs fed the duck. | | |
| Pam digs and digs. | | |

**Write it.**

pen

Find the picture that begins with
the sound of each letter below.
"X" it.

| | | | |
|---|---|---|---|
| ă | | | |
| ĕ | | $2 + 2 = 4$ | |
| ĭ | | | |
| ŭ | | | |
| ĕ | | | $\begin{array}{r} 2 \\ +\ 2 \\ \hline 4 \end{array}$ |
| ĭ | | 8 | |

"X" the same word.

| | | | |
|---|---|---|---|
| tip | lip | ~~tip~~ | tap |
| hum | ham | hug | hum |
| jug | jag | jug | jab |
| kid | hip | hid | kid |
| Sal | Sat | Sell | Sal |
| get | get | gut | gal |
| sis | sip | sis | sit |

Read, copy, and "X" it.

| tip <br> t i p | | | |
|---|---|---|---|
| six <br> _ _ _ | | 6 | |
| fun <br> _ _ _ | | | |
| beg <br> _ _ _ | | | |
| Kim <br> _ _ _ | | | |
| web <br> _ _ _ | | | |
| Jeff <br> _ _ _ _ | | | JAM |

70

Spell.                                    Write.

| | | | | |
|---|---|---|---|---|
| k (t) a (i) b (p) | | | | **tip** |
| w p e u g b | | | | |
| d l e a g p | | | | |
| m n i u t l | | | | |
| m b a e t g | | | | |
| h s i u d p | | | | |
| m z i e p n | | | | |

71

Match and write it.

| Kim | beg | wet | nut |
|-----|-----|-----|-----|
| ~~tip~~ | fell | hid | zip |

tip

◯ it.

| | tim |
|---|---|
| | (tip) |
| | top |

| | wed | | nip |
|---|---|---|---|
| | web | | nap |
| | wet | | net |

| | met | | Deb |
|---|---|---|---|
| | wet | | fed |
| | wit | | bed |

| | six | | bed |
|---|---|---|---|
| | zip | | bid |
| | set | | bud |

73

"X" it.

| | | |
|---|---|---|
| Peg is ten.<br><br>The can is tin. | ☒<br>☐ | |
| Jen will fix the big ax.<br><br>Jen will pass the nuts. | ☐<br>☐ | |
| Ted tips the cup.<br><br>Ted met his pal. | ☐<br>☐ | |
| Kim hid in a jug.<br><br>Kim hugs the pet. | ☐<br>☐ | |
| A big, wet bag fell.<br><br>A bug sat in the web. | ☐<br>☐ | |
| Deb has ten legs.<br><br>Deb has fun. | ☐<br>☐ | |
| The big pup begs us.<br><br>The pup tips its hat. | ☐<br>☐ | |

**Write it.**

tip – – – – – – – – – – – – – – – – – –

*For further practice on short a, i, u, and e combined, see Book 1½, pp. 57–64.

75

# o says /ŏ/ as in

Find the picture that begins with
the sound of each letter below.
"X" it.

| ŏ | | | |
|---|---|---|---|
| ă | | | |
| ŏ | | | |
| ĭ | | | |
| ŏ | | | |
| ĕ | | | |

Follow the arrows to write the letter **o**, which says /ŏ/ as in .
Say the sound aloud.

Notice that **o** is only one space tall. Trace the letters.

Trace and copy the letter that begins the pictured word.

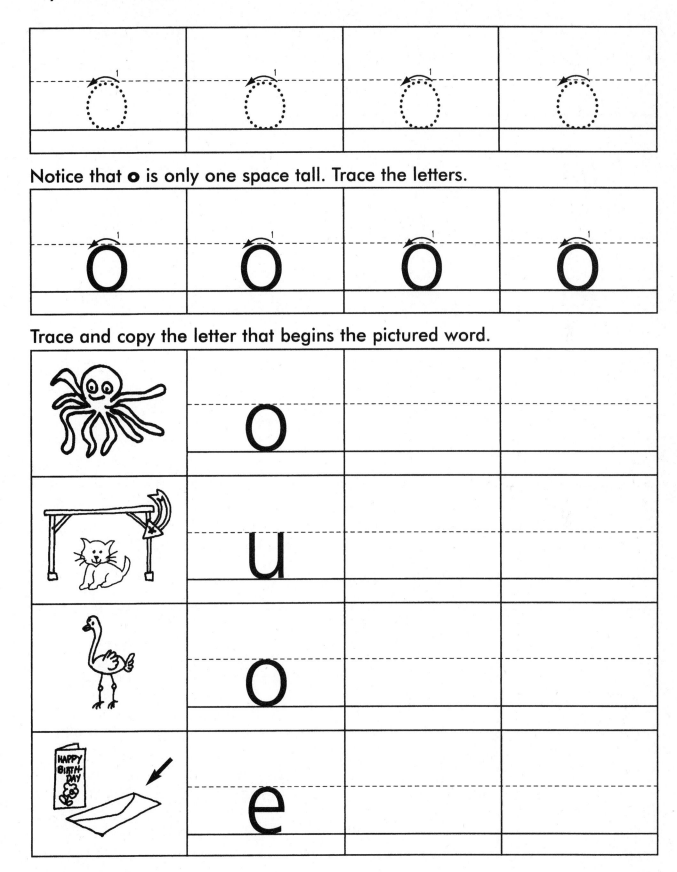

"X" the same word.

| | | | |
|---|---|---|---|
| log | leg | fog | ~~log~~ |
| lot | let | lot | tot |
| job | jog | job | jab |
| rot | not | rut | rot |
| mob | mob | nob | mad |
| not | nut | not | ton |
| Tom | Tod | Ton | Tom |

78

Read, copy, and "X" it.

| log **l o g** | | | (X) |
|---|---|---|---|
| fox ___ ___ ___ | | | |
| cop ___ ___ ___ | | | |
| rob ___ ___ ___ | | | |
| top ___ ___ ___ | | | |
| mom ___ ___ ___ | | | |
| pot ___ ___ ___ | | | |

Match and write it.

rip     pot     mom     ~~log~~

rod     mop     hop     box

log _ _ _ _ _ _ _

Spell.                                              Write.

| | | | | |
|---|---|---|---|---|
| (l) t | a (o) | p (g) | **log** |
| b d | o a | n x | |
| m n | o a | n m | |
| p d | o a | t l | |
| f t | o u | x n | |
| r n | a o | b d | |
| c t | o u | p b | |

lug

( log )

leg

| | | | | |
|---|---|---|---|---|
| | hop | | | mop |
| | tot | | | map |
| | hot | | | nap |
| | rib | | | hog |
| | rub | | | nap |
| | rob | | | hop |
| | Bob | | | dug |
| | bib | | | dog |
| | bed | | | fog |

"X" it.

| | | |
|---|---|---|
| A cat is in a hot tub.<br><br>A log is in a pot. | ☒<br>☐ | |
| Jill pats the wet dog.<br><br>Jill has a hot dog. | ☐<br>☐ | |
| The cop sits on a box.<br><br>The cop sits on a fox. | ☐<br>☐ | |
| Pam fills the pot.<br><br>Pam can sit on the log. | ☐<br>☐ | |
| The dog is on the box.<br><br>The box is on the dog. | ☐<br>☐ | |
| The mop will fix the mess.<br><br>The pig sits in the mess. | ☐<br>☐ | |
| The pup sits on the hog.<br><br>The fox hops on the log. | ☐<br>☐ | |

Write it.

log

Find the picture that begins with
the sound of each letter below.
"X" it.

| | | | |
|---|---|---|---|
| ĕ | $+\dfrac{2}{2} \; \dfrac{}{4}$ | | |
| ŏ | | | |
| ă | | | |
| ĭ | | | |
| ŭ | | | |
| ĕ | | | |

"X" the same word.

| | | | |
|---|---|---|---|
| rat | cat | ~~rat~~ | rag |
| pop | pep | pop | pup |
| pack | pick | pack | peck |
| led | lid | led | lad |
| sick | sack | sick | sock |
| rock | rock | rack | mock |
| luck | lock | tuck | luck |

Match and write it.

bib     ~~rat~~     duck     kick

well     lock     neck     doll

rat

| | | | | |
|---|---|---|---|---|
| | c  r̃  ã  o  f  t̃ | | | **rat** |
| | n  m  e  i | b  ck | | |
| | m  w  e  i | ck  ll | | |
| | t  k  i  e | ck  ss | | |
| | l  t  a  o | z  ck | | |
| | b  d  o  u | ck  g | | |
| | d  b  e  o | ll  ck | | |

Yes or no?

| | No | Yes |
|---|---|---|
| Can Jim sip pop? | ☐ | ☒ |
| Can a doll run? | ☐ | ☐ |
| Will Jill sit on a rat? | ☐ | ☐ |
| Can a duck get a wig? | ☐ | ☐ |
| Can a well kick? | ☐ | ☐ |
| Will a hat fit Jeff? | ☐ | ☐ |
| Will a big tub hop? | ☐ | ☐ |

"X" it.

| | | |
|---|---|---|
| It is a big lock.<br><br>Dot has a red sock. | ☒<br>☐ | |
| The pig led Jim to the lock.<br><br>The pig locks Jim in the bus. | ☐<br>☐ | |
| The men sell a hen in a pen.<br><br>The duck met a cat at the well. | ☐<br>☐ | |
| Pat fell and hit his leg.<br><br>Pam kicks a can on the hill. | ☐<br>☐ | |
| Jill sits on a wet duck.<br><br>Jeff has a wet bug on his back. | ☐<br>☐ | |
| The mutt has a bell on its neck.<br><br>The mutt met a duck on a log. | ☐<br>☐ | |
| Bill will lock the dog pen.<br><br>Bill kicks the bag of rags. | ☐<br>☐ | |

Write it.

rat

**Write it.**

*For further practice, see Book 1½, pp. 73–88.

| | |
|---|---|
| 1. hop<br>hip<br>hog | 2. wed<br>web<br>wet |
| 3. sill<br>fill<br>hill | 4. cup<br>cap<br>cop |
| 5. dad<br>bad<br>dab | 6. bug<br>big<br>beg |
| 7. his<br>him<br>hum | 8. mat<br>men<br>met |

1. _____

2. _____

3. _____

4. _____

5. _____

◯ it.

1. A hen can   red.
   run.
   rut.

2. I can sip from a   cub.
   cud.
   cup.

3. The sun is big and   hit
   hat.
   hot.

4. The rug has a   rap.
   rip.
   rod.

5. An ax can cut a   log.
   lag.
   lug.

6. I will nap on a   bud.
   bed.
   bid.

Read and "X" it.

1. I can sit and run and beg. I can
   dig up a rib and tug on a mat.
   I am a pal and a pet. I am a

   pop.

   pup.

   pep.

2. Tom will fill it and mix in it. Tom
   has ham in it and a lid on top. If it
   tips, it is a mess! It is a

   pet.

   pit.

   pot.